Handwriting

Key Stage 1
For ages 5-7

Practise & Learn

Published by CGP

Editors:
Holly Corfield-Carr
Luke Antieul
Jennifer Underwood

With thanks to Luke von Kotze and
Jill Cousner for the proofreading.

ISBN: 978 1 84762 743 8
Groovy website: www.cgpbooks.co.uk
Printed by Elanders Ltd, Newcastle upon Tyne
Jolly bits of clipart from CORELDRAW®

Contents

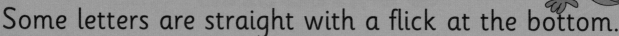

Some letters are straight with a flick at the bottom.

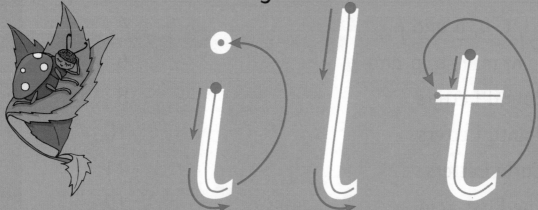

Trace these letters.
Start at the red blob and follow the arrows.

Trace the pattern and copy it across the page.

Trace the letters and copy them across the page.

4

Here are some more letters for you to trace.

u y j

These might be a bit more
tricky, so follow the red arrows carefully.

Trace the pattern and copy it across the page.

u u u u u u u u u u u u u

y y y y y

j j j j

l i t l i t

j u l y j u l y

5

h, n, m, r, b, p and k

These letters start with a straight line.
Trace down and back up the line.

h n m r

Halfway back up the line follow the arrows to make a branch. Trace the rest of the letter.

Trace the letters and copy them across the page.

h h h h

n n n n

m m m

r r r r

The branches on these letters loop all the way round.
Trace the letters. Start from the red blob.

Trace the letters and copy them across the page.

b b b b

p p p p

k k k k

Trace the word and copy it.

bumpy

Round Letters

These letters all start with a round shape.

Trace the letters.
Start at the red blob and follow the arrows.

Trace the letters and copy them across the page.

c c c c . . . .

a a a a . . . .

o o o o . . . .

e e e e . . . .

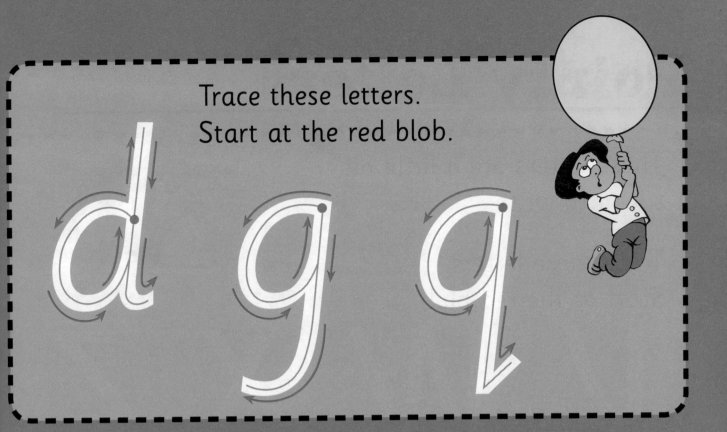

Trace these letters.
Start at the red blob.

Trace the letters and copy them across the page.

d d d d

g g g g

q q q q

Trace the word and copy it.

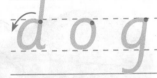

d o g

Pointy Letters

These letters are a little bit tricky to write.

Trace these letters.
Start at the red blob.

U W X Z

Trace the letters and copy them across the page.

U U U U

W W W W

X X X X

Z Z Z Z

Curly Letters

Curly letters are tricky but they are also fun.

Practise tracing curly letters. Start at the red blob.

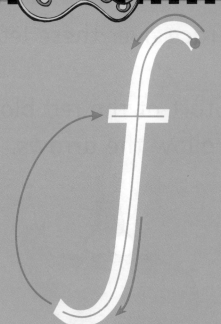

Trace the letters and copy them across the page.

s s s s

f f f f

Trace the word and copy it.

vase

The First Join

Trace over these letters to join the **a** to the **n**.

Start at the red blob.
Follow the arrows.

Trace and copy the letters to practise the joins.

an   an an

um   um um

ir   ir ir

up   up up

si   si si

Trace and copy the words to practise the joins.

cup cup

sun sun

dip dip

map map

sip sip

mum mum

Trace and copy the sentence.

a tiny mum jumps up

a tiny mum jumps up

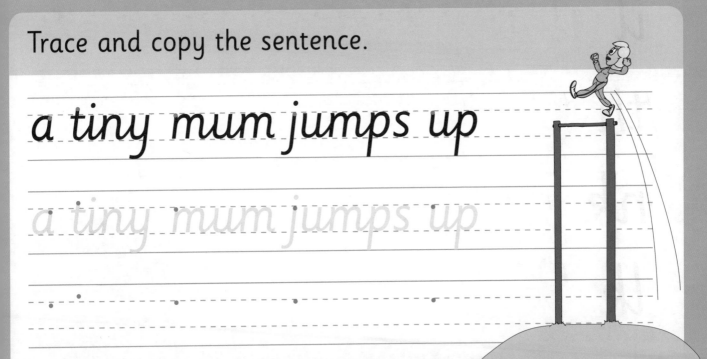

13

The Second Join

Trace over these letters to join the **a** to the **t**.

Start at the red blob.
Follow the arrows.

 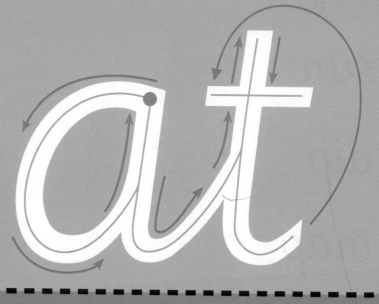

Trace and copy the letters to practise the joins.

at at at

il il il

th th th

nk nk nk

lk lk lk

14

Trace and copy the words to practise the joins.

cut   *cut*

all   *all*

ink   *ink*

bull   *bull*

ill   *ill*

built   *built*

Trace and copy the sentence.

an ill bull up a hill

an ill bull up a hill

The Third Join

Trace over these letters to join the **t** to the **o**.

Start at the red blob.
Follow the arrows.

Remember to cross
the **t** when you
finish the join.

Trace and copy the letters to practise the joins.

to   to to

da   da da

nd   nd nd

ag   ag ag

as   as as

Trace and copy the words to practise the joins.

dad   dad

cat   cat

ear   ear

hand   hand

salt   salt

Trace and copy the sentence.

mum and dad each had a cat

mum and dad each had a cat

The Fourth Join

Trace over these letters to join the **o** to the **r**.

Start at the red blob.
Follow the arrows.

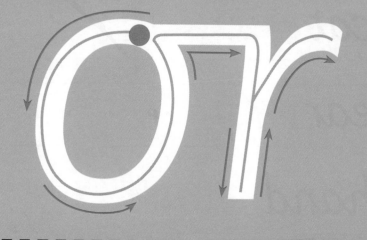

Trace and copy the letters to practise the joins.

or or or

we we we

vi vi vi

ry ry ry

fi fi fi

Trace and copy the words to practise the joins.

win   *win*

fry   *fry*

trip   *trip*

very   *very*

torn   *torn*

five   *five*

Trace and copy the sentence.

we love to find treasure

we love to find treasure

19

The Fifth Join

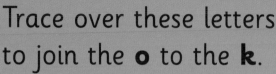

Trace over these letters to join the **o** to the **k**.

Start at the red blob. Follow the arrows.

Trace and copy the letters to practise the joins.

ok   ok

ot   ot

rl   rl

wh   wh

of   of

Trace and copy the words to practise the joins.

what   *what*

cart   *cart*

not   *not*

cork   *cork*

dot   *dot*

Trace and copy the sentence.

very smart sharks are

not scared of the dark

The Sixth Join

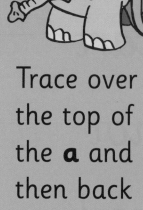

Trace over these letters to join the **w** to the **a**.

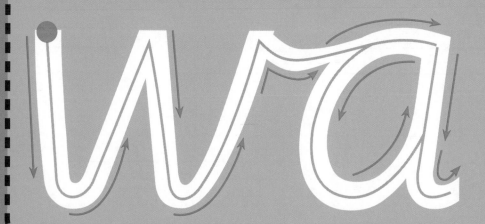

Trace over the top of the **a** and then back round.

Trace and copy the letters to practise the joins.

wa *wa*

oo *oo*

oa *oa*

rc *rc*

og *og*

Trace and copy the words to practise the joins.

dog   dog

coat   coat

room   room

word   word

face   face

wave   wave

Trace and copy the sentence.

it took two steps forward

Break Letters

You don't have to join to the next letter after any of these letters.

b g j p

Trace and copy these words. Don't join all the letters.

busy *busy*

green *green*

jumper *jumper*

piglet *piglet*

page *page*

These letters also don't have to join to the next letter.

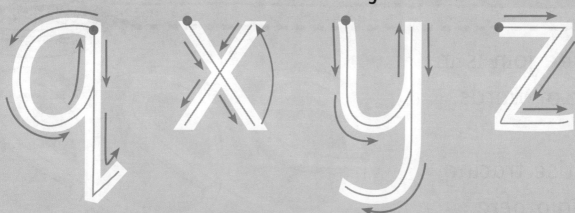

Trace and copy these words. Don't join all the letters.

quick   quick

boxes   boxes

zipped   zipped

the biggest zebra eats the

most jelly

Common Joins

The **ee** join is in a lot of words.

Practise tracing the join here.

eee

Trace and copy.

eee *eee* · · · · ·

en *en* · · · · et *et* · · · ·

re *re* · · · me *me* · · · ·

see *see* · · ·

feet *feet* · · · · · ·

creep *creep* · · ·

These pairs of letters are common in words.

ch sh th wh

Trace and copy these sentences.

chirpy chicks munch chips

she dashes in shiny shoes

they think maths is great

the white whale whistles

Capital Letters

Capital letters don't need to join to any other letters.
Capital letters are bigger than normal letters.

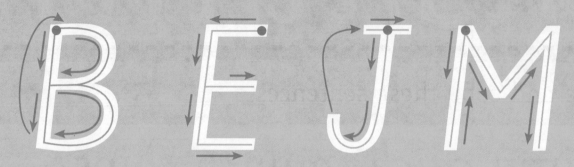

Trace and copy the capital letters.

A A A   B B B   C C C

D D D   E E E   F F F

G G G   H H H   I I I

J J J   K K K   L L L

M M M   N N N   O O O

P P P   Q Q Q   R R R

Trace and copy the capital letters.

S S T T

U U V V W W

X X Y Y Z Z

Trace and copy. Don't join the capital letters.

Tom went to London

It rained all of Monday

He visits Canada in May

Writing Practice

I went to the park
To play on the swings
But then I heard
The flutter of wings.

A big scary dragon,
All scaly and blue,
Whizzed down the slide
And away he flew.

I went to the park

To play on the swings

But then I heard

The flutter of wings.

A big scary dragon,

All scaly and blue,

Whizzed down the slide

And away he flew.

More Writing Practice

Copy the paragraph below in joined handwriting.

My family are going on holiday to France this summer. We are staying in a hotel by the sea. I am looking forward to going to the beach and hunting for sea shells. I also want to eat lots of French bread!